Sick and Tired of Being Sick and Tired

by
PHILIP L. HANSEN

M & M PRINTING, INC.
Minneapolis, Minnesota
1977

SICK AND TIRED
OF BEING SICK AND TIRED

M & M Printing, Inc.
Minneapolis, Minnesota

Library of Congress Number 77-181-099
Printed and bound in the United States of America

Introduction

The Body of Christ has many wounds; one of the worst is alcoholism. It is beyond doubt, in my mind, the number one public health problem in our society today. I know of no illness that affects more people, primarily and secondarily, and reaches its destructive tentacles into more segments of our society than alcoholism.

This book is an attempt to say some things about the people who suffer from alcoholism in such a way that the reader may gain better insight into the enormity of this illness. I chose the story of the Prodigal Son as the vehicle to carry what I have tried to say because man's oldest illness and the greatest story ever told belong together.

It should be pointed out that I have referred to the alcoholic as "he" throughout the book. I hope this will in no way distract from the female alcoholic in our society. At least in the metropolitan areas of our country we are told that there is a woman alcoholic for every male alcoholic. The female alcoholic needs help and the dynamics of her identification, treatment, and rehabilitation are essentially the same as that of the male alcoholic.

I am indebted to many for whatever insight and skill I may possess in the area of alcohol problems. My parents, Pastor and Mrs. Harold Hansen, planted the seed of concern for alcohol problems early in my life and watered it while they raised me in their household. Redeemer Lutheran Congregation in White Bear Lake, Minnesota enabled me and encouraged me to work in this area of social concern. For twelve years I served them as pastor and shall forever be grateful for their love and understanding. For ten of the twelve years I served as pastor of Redeemer I was a clergy consultant to the Hazelden Foundation. Hazelden provided me with the treatment setting where I was able to delve more intensively into the illness of alcoholism. While at Hazelden it was my privilege to meet and know thousands of alcoholics from all over the world. I appreciate those years.* My great debt, however, is to the individual alcoholic for all he taught me about myself.

What I am saying can best be said with this bit of wisdom given to me by an alcoholic:

> After all, what did I possess in life beyond my ability to hear, to see and some skill in carrying out what I had learned?
> I have learned from wise men, from fools, broadminded men, children and ripe seniors.

*I acknowledge with thanks Mrs. Rosalie Hansen and Mrs. Elaine Koob for the hours they spent proofreading and typing the original manuscript.

They came to me and told me what struck them
and all I had to do was reap that which
had been sown before me.

It is to the individual alcoholic, drunk or
sober, that I dedicate this book.

Luke 15:11-24
(*Revised Standard Version*)

And he said, "There was a man who had two sons; and the younger of them said to his Father, 'Father, give me the share of property that falls to me.' And he divided his living between them. Not many days later, the younger son gathered all he had and took his journey into a far country, and there he squandered his property in loose living. And when he had spent everything, a great famine arose in that country, and he began to be in want. So he went and joined himself to one of the citizens of that country, who sent him into his fields to feed swine. And he would gladly have fed on the pods that the swine ate; and no one gave him anything. But when he came to himself he said, 'How many of my father's servants have bread enough and to spare, but I perish here with hunger! I will arise and go to my father, and I will say to him, "Father, I have sinned against heaven and before you; I am no longer worthy to be called your son; treat me as one of your hired servants." ' And he arose and came to his father. But while he was yet at a distance, his father saw him and had compassion, and ran and embraced him and kissed him. And the son said to him, 'Father, I have sinned against heaven and before you; I am no longer worthy to be called your son.' But the father said to his servants, 'Bring quickly the best robe, and put it on him; and put a ring on his hand, and shoes on his feet; and bring the fatted calf and kill it, and let us eat and make merry; for this my son was dead, and is alive again; he was lost, and is found.' And they began to make merry.

Table of Contents

The Twelve Steps of Alcoholics Anonymous

Step One: *"We admitted we were power-less over alcohol—that our lives had become unman-ageable."*

Step Two: *"Came to believe that a Power greater than ourselves could restore us to sanity."*

Step Three: *"Made a decision to turn our will and our lives over to the care of God as we un-derstood Him."*

Step Four: *"Made a searching and fearless moral inventory of our-selves."*

Step Five: *"Admitted to God, to ourselves, and to another human be-ing, the exact nature of our wrongs."*

Step Six: *"Were entirely ready to have God remove all these defects of character."*

Step Seven: *"Humbly asked Him to remove our shortcomings."*

Step Eight: *"Made a list of all persons we had harmed, and become willing to make amends to them all."*

Step Nine: *"Made direct amends to such people whenever possible, except when to do so would injure them or others."*

Step Ten: *"Continued to take personal inventory and when we were wrong promptly admitted it."*

Step Eleven: *"Sought through prayer and meditation to improve our conscious contact with God as we understood Him, praying only for knowledge of His will for us and the power to carry that out."*

Step Twelve: *"Having had a spiritual awakening as the result of these steps, we tried to carry this message to alcoholics and to practice these principles in all our affairs."*

Chapter I

Sick of Home

The Prodigal Son was an alcoholic; he was a phony; he was a lush!

It is impossible to prove that the young fellow we know as the Prodigal Son in Jesus' parable ever had a drink of ethyl alcohol, but if alcoholism is a living problem more than a drinking problem, then there can be little doubt about his alcoholism. This can be substantiated by the accepted idea that a person is drunk mentally before he is drunk physically, just as one commits adultery mentally before becoming physically involved. "Stinking Thinking Causes Stinking Drinking" is an old adage among Alcoholics Anonymous members. We can learn more about this young man's alcohol dependency by keeping our eyes on his behavior than by watching what, when, and how much he drinks.

Ethyl alcohol, the common denominator in all alcoholic beverage, has been used longer, historically, and by more people, numerically, than any other depressant or mood modifier known to man. The oldest decipherable clay tablet contains a recipe for the making of alcoholic beverage. Because it is such a volatile chemical when introduced into the blood stream, it has naturally caused some very heated disagreements over the years regarding its use, non-use, and abuse. When you consider the ambivalent feelings that we have about this chemical in each of us and in our society, it would be more correct to call it an emotion rather than a chemical.

One of the most descriptive illustrations I have seen of this emotional ambivalence around ethyl alcohol is exemplified in the story of the elderly lady who confronted her clergyman with the regret that wine was being used in the Sacrament. When she was reminded that Jesus drank wine, she nodded and said, "Yes, and that's the one thing I don't like about Jesus!"

Is it any wonder that a chemical which is elevated to Sacramental status on the one hand and labeled as the Devil's Scourge on the other will arouse some deep emotion? What I would like to suggest at this point is that perhaps both points of view are correct in their own sphere of reference. Too long the "wets" and the "drys" have looked across the chasm and thanked God that they weren't like the other. Today, as never before, the dividing wall is coming down between the users and the non-users of ethyl alcohol, and both are focusing their common concern on the problems that can arise from the use of alcohol. Certainly everyone should be concerned about such problems as: *Alcoholism, Alcohol and the Impaired Driver, Alcohol and the Adolescent, The Chronic Drunkenness Offender,* and realistic *Alcohol Legislation* whether they use this chemical or not.

There is a word in the English language that can be used to describe the exact opposite of what it means; that word is CLEAVE. Cleave means, on the one hand, to draw together, as it is used in Genesis 2:24, "Therefore a man leaves his father and his mother and CLEAVES to his wife, and they become one flesh." Most commonly, however, we think of cleaving as separating or parting. In like manner, I would like to suggest that the chemical ethyl alcohol has both divided us and drawn us together. Historically, every profession and discipline has seen the problem of alcoholism from their own bias, and felt they had the answer to the problem. This attitude only divided the disciplines farther apart, and drove the alcohol dependent person deeper into his despair. The clergyman warned the alcoholic that if he didn't quit drinking he would go to hell; the doctor said he would die; the psychiatrist said he would go crazy; the wife said she would leave; and the employer said he would fire him. The alcoholic responded: "What else is new?"

In 1935, the first ray of hope for the chronic alcoholic came across the horizon with the advent of Alcoholics Anonymous (A.A.). Alcoholics Anonymous is a world wide fellowship of men and women who are banded together to solve their common problems and to help bring fellow sufferers to recovery from the age-old baffling malady, alcoholism. The Twelve Steps of A.A. are a group of principles that are spiritual in nature, which, if practiced as a way of life, can enable the sufferer to overcome the obsession to drink and restore him to happiness and usefulness. A.A. could be called many things, but it is certainly the greatest out-patient, peer-group, therapy the world has ever known. Actually, they have taken the term, "Communion of Saints," and made it live in such a way that the Christian Church, which coined the phrase in the first place, should blush. It would be difficult to deny that A.A. has fulfilled the command of St. Paul when he said in his letter to the Galatians (6:2), "Bear one another's burdens, and so fulfill the law of Christ."

With the advent of A.A. and the thrusting of alcoholism into the limelight as an illness and public health problem, this same malady that has divided us, individually and collectively, is now drawing us together in a common concern.

There are those who find it difficult to acknowledge that alcoholism is an illness. They are prone to say that if it is an illness, how come so many are trying to catch it. Another over-simplification for arresting this illness can be heard by those who say that if these people had enough will-power and back-bone, they could quit. To this I would tend to reply that the next time they are suffering from diarrhea, it would be interesting to see how effective will-power and back-bone would be in that instance.

It might be well to define alcoholism at this point. There are as many definitions as there are people defining it. For all practical purposes, every definition is correct because it is that kind of an illness. Having heard many definitions, I would say simply that alcoholism is lack or loss of control around the chemical ethyl alcohol. The person who suffers from alcoholism cannot, in fact, choose whether he will drink or not, and once he has taken a drink, he can no longer predict his future behavior. The old saying is correct that "One drink is too many, and a thousand are too few." Alcoholics are people who lose their tolerance for ethyl alcohol and become mentally and physically preoccupied with this chemical.

One of the hindrances to early diagnosis and treatment of alcoholism is that we have tended to equate this illness with skid-row behavior when, in fact, this is not the truth. There are indeed alcoholics who may descend into the skid-row environment for a period during their illness, but this is more the exception than the rule. The generally accepted statistics indicate that 3% of alcoholics are on skid-row, while 97% live, work, worship and play where the rest of society lives. Most alcoholics still hold their jobs, their families, and their social status despite the progressive deterioration caused by their drinking.

This skid-row "template" of the alcoholic is perhaps the most difficult obstacle to overcome in helping the alcoholic to an awareness of his illness. If we wait until the alcoholic manifests some kind of skid-row behavior, we will have missed the overwhelming majority of those afflicted. This kind of behavior could be likened to someone doing nothing about the common cold until it had developed into pneumonia.

If you studied one-hundred alcoholics you would discover one-hundred different types of drinkers. The only factor that would be the same in all is that they lose control after taking a drink, and this loss of control has created a sustaining problem in some area of their lives.

The Prodigal Son is a case in point: he came from a fine household and might be representative of any one of us—our strata of society, our occupation or age group. Those who wait for a person to hit some undefineable point in his drinking behavior before they consider him an alcohol dependent, only prolong the agony and reduce the prognosis for rehabilitation. I shall spend more time in a later chapter on the whole subject of intervention and the creation of crisis.

There isn't a doubt in my mind but what Alcoholism is the Number One public health problem in our society. When you take into consideration those who are affected as well as those who are afflicted, and when you consider the physical, moral, social, spiritual and vocational damage that it brings, it must be conceded that it has no peer among the illnesses.

It is not only the Number One health problem, but I also believe it to be the most Satanic illness in our midst. If I were called upon to point out examples of demon possession in our civilization, I would begin with alcoholism because some of the manifestations of this illness could only be conceived by the Evil One. What other illness, for instance, causes one to hurt most those people whom he loves the most? This is true to the point that when you want to know whom he loves the most, you ask whom he has hurt the most by his drinking. What other illness will cause one to lie when it is easier to tell the truth? What other illness will cause one to manifest anti-social behavior of all kinds when these would be the last things he would do sober? I would rather fall victim to any other illness of which I am aware than to be a victim of alcoholism.

It is because of the repulsive behavior of the alcoholic that we have tended to moralize this illness rather than treat it. We have tended to keep our eye on the behavior of the victim instead of the illness that causes such behavior. We cannot intellectualize, moralize, or threaten this illness; it must be treated. The alcoholic who is threatened with hell might well respond that you can't go to hell when you have already been there for five years, or ten years, or however long this hell has lasted. It has been estimated that for every alcoholic who has found sobriety there are seven who are still living in that labyrinth of despair. We must get to these people and help them to understand that they are sick, that they have an illness that is treatable, and that they are worth treating.

It is my theory that the Prodigal Son was an alcoholic, and if we read between the lines, I think we will discover some alcoholic behavior long before he left home or even before he took his first drink. I have heard alcoholics say they were alcoholic psychologically long before they ever had their first drink.

The young man in the parable was just plain sick of home. He had had enough of discipline, routine, security, and all the comforts of home. He could stand no more. He wanted to get out where the action was.

There is no indication that he disliked his parents or his home; apparently he just wanted out. He is, however, manifesting self-centeredness. In other words, he is seeing himself, his needs, his problems, his desires as the center of all existence. This young man was rapidly becoming a spiritual hump-back examining his own navel. It is more than likely that he was beginning to manifest some paranoid ideas. In the normal course of events when he was corrected or disciplined, he saw himself more picked upon than corrected and guided. He became drenched in self-pity when he recognized in others what he failed to achieve for himself, and became envious of these people. As a result, he established his own "poor me" society.

Often it seems that the alcoholic is trying to recapture the teen-age years of life. For some reasons, he tends to think he has missed out on something. One alcoholic put it this way to me: he said he had a wonderful childhood—all 52 years of it. One of the most difficult things in arresting alcoholism is that this person who has been acting like a child must now accept adult responsibility. Ordinarily this is done in the normal trauma of change from adolescence to adulthood, but for the alcoholic it must be a revolutionary kind of change.

Another characteristic of the alcoholic is the desire for comfort. He tends to turn to those things which smooth the rough edges off reality. When he discovers the euphoria of ethyl alcohol, he tends to rely on it for comfort and establish a mood that will enable him to be more comfortable in reality. It is at this point that it ceases to be a beverage and is now a self-administered medicinal drug.

An arrested alcoholic said to me on one occasion, regarding alcohol, "My best friend betrayed me!" What he said was that over the years alcohol had done exactly what he wanted it to do for him. When the reward turned into punishment, and the chemical that enabled him to live comfortably with reality threatened his very existence, he realized he was a chronically ill man. The word "need" is the key word in this chemical dependency game. When the drinking person says, "I need a drink!" the flags should go up.

People, both young and old, who drink are often concerned that they will become problem drinkers, and wonder what the difference between social drinking and problem drinking is. The best definition I have heard is that a social drinker is one who goes to a social event, whatever it may be, and in the process may *incidentally* drink an alcoholic beverage. This means he would have gone to the social event were there drinking or not. The problem drinker, on the other hand, is someone who goes somewhere to drink and may *incidentally* socialize. This simple measure of a person's drinking might prove helpful in differentiating use from abuse.

If I understand this young man in our parable as manifesting typical alcoholic behavior, then maybe I'd better describe him and his background a little better. He isn't a bad boy; in fact, in many ways, he is a good boy. He has a zest for living that needs to be expressed. He comes from a disciplined background which tends to make him rather rigid morally: right is right, and wrong is wrong, and never the twain shall meet. When all is as it ought to be, he is a kind of judge and jury and conscience for everyone in the vicinity. He is a punctual person; when he goes somewhere he wants to be on time, if not a few minutes early. He is rarely late for anything and will often stay late to give good measure. He also tends to be a perfectionist. "If you do a thing, do it right," is his motto, and he gets upset when others don't care or do a half-way job on something. He is a loyal person who bears allegiance to those meaningful relationships and institutions in his life. He tends to be a lover instead of a fighter, and can woo a bird off a branch.

This sounds like the father, mother, friend, employee, etc., we have been looking for, and rightly so; but all these traits apply only to sobriety. When this fellow I have described is drinking and involved in chronic alcoholism, all these things turn 180 degrees. Many a wife has said to me that when her husband is not drinking, he is the finest husband a woman could ask for; but when he takes a drink, he just changes into something or someone else. The little verse:

> "There was a little girl
> Who had a pretty curl
> Right in the middle of her forehead.
> When she was good
> She was very, very good
> But when she was bad,
> She was horrid."

is a good description of the alcoholic person

when he is drinking and when he is not.

When the young man in the beginning of the parable says, "Father, give me my share of the property," he is saying much more about himself than meets the eye. Later developments bear this out.

Maybe, just maybe, Jesus is trying to tell us about alcoholism in this parable and doesn't want to confuse it with drinking behavior; or maybe he is saying there is alcoholic behavior in every one of us, only our hang-ups may be something other than alcohol.

Countless times it has been said by both members and non-members of A.A., "You can take the first step out of the twelve steps of A.A., and the A.A. Way of Life is good for anyone."

If the Prodigals of every generation could accept this thesis, prevention would take on new meaning and much human misery would be avoided.

Chapter II

The Stay-at-Homes

The Father decided to let the son go. It says simply, "So he divided his estate between them." I'm certain that the Father took the young man aside and told him how much they would miss him; how one day he would manage the estate. The Father did what any parent would do to convince the child he loved to remain at home.

But this young man's mind is made up, and he is not about to be reversed in his desire to get away from home and out where all the action is. So the Father lets him go. Really, the Father lets go. This Father is as possessive as any other father, but when he realizes that his son's mind is made up, he lets go. His love will never stop, to be sure, but now he will no longer be able to see and touch and serve and talk to this one he loves so much. How it must have broken his heart when he let him go; but let him go he did and this, in the final analysis, was perhaps the wisest thing he had ever done.

The Father in the parable is a symbol of those we can call the "Stay-at-homes"—the people who surround the alcoholic and are caught up in the tragic illness. We want to concern ourselves in this chapter with their illness, their need for help, and their role in the recovery of the alcoholic.

Most of the time the clergyman, the doctor, the social worker, and others will be dealing with the spouse of the alcoholic. To be married to an alcoholic is to become sick also. To have an alcoholic parent is to be a sick child. To be emotionally involved in any meaningful way with an alcoholic is to become a sick person.

Think of the guilt a wife experiences, for instance, as she watches this person she loves slide into chronic alcohol dependency with all of its perverse behavior. Maybe, she thinks to herself, if I had been a better wife this would never have happened; and while she is thinking this to herself, the alcoholic husband is assuring her that she IS the cause of all his problems.

How often must she call his employer and lie about his being sick when the real problem is his intoxication or hangover? Perhaps she has had to bail him out of jail when he was arrested for driving while intoxicated, or for causing a disturbance, or for starting a brawl, or for some other scrape with the law. On occasion she has possibly had to cover a bad check that he has cashed while drinking. In most instances, they are already in a financial bind so she may have taken money from the children's bank account or from any other source possible to cover the deficit. She has tried on any number of occasions to shelter the children from the alcoholic father's temper tantrums, and tried for as long as she can to maintain their respect for him.

The children fear to bring anyone into their home for fear their parent may be drunk and embarrass them. All in all the family is falling apart until the wife just gives up in despair.

Because we have failed to identify this illness early, it is often at this point that the spouse will contact a clergyman, doctor, lawyer, or some other professional when great damage and deterioration has already been done to every member of the family. The most common remark I have heard as a pastor working with the spouse of the alcoholic is that she just doesn't care anymore—for all practical purposes the spouse is void of emotion; she can't cry; she can't get angry; she can't laugh; she is an extremely sick person.

The therapist, or professional of any kind, who fails to recognize that this is a family illness, will never really do justice to the total recovery of all the sick people involved. It took me longer than I care to admit to counsel and give help to the person whom I was talking to on the phone or sitting with in my office. The temptation is to talk about the husband's drinking, what he ought to do, and what we can do to help him, etc. This person you are talking to needs help whether the alcoholic spouse ever gets help or not.

This became clear to me some years ago when I was called by a woman to come and talk to her husband who had a drinking problem. I consented to do so, and arrived a few minutes later. He was sitting in a chair in one corner, feeling no pain, while she sat on the other side of the room on the piano stool. I made up the third point in the triangle.

The husband had very little to say, which is typical. He wanted to see me like he wanted another hole in his head.

She began rather typically to read his inventory, and tell of all their problems which his drinking had caused. As she progressed, she got louder and louder, until she was actually yelling at both of us.

When she paused to catch her breath, I seized the opportunity to interrupt, "If my wife yelled like you do, I'd be tempted to go out and get drunk, too." The husband looked at me in unbelief! Apparently I had spoken his thoughts as well.

What I learned that day was that I was in the room with two sick people—TWO sick people —who both needed help. Their illnesses were different, and the kind of help they needed was different, but to ignore that basic need for help in either would not be fair.

The choices for the spouse of the alcoholic are quite simple. If the husband is the alcoholic, the wife must learn either to live with him or without him. The opposite would also be true where the wife is the alcoholic. Carrying out either of these decisions is most difficult and emotion laden.

First, the spouse should join the fellowship organization called ALANON. Alanon is a God-send if ever there was one! This organization is for the spouse, the parent, the relative, or even a friend of the alcoholic. The program is exactly the same as A.A., but here the common problem is having a loved one who is an alcohol dependent person.

By helping one another understand the illness, alcoholism, and their own illness as the result of it, they assist in helping their counterparts in being restored to sanity. They learn that pouring their mate's bottle down the sink, or yelling at them at the top of their voice isn't helping either. In fact, it's only making matters worse.

You can say that Alanon is helping the spouse, or others, to do what the Father in the parable did—let the alcoholic go. Needless to say, this isn't any easier for the spouse than it was for the Father in Jesus' parable.

If you look, or even listen, closely you will discover that behind every alcoholic there is that person we call the "enabler." This is the person who enables the sick alcoholic to continue in his illness, to continue in his uncontrolled behavior around alcohol. More times than not you can hear these enablers before you can see them, for they are most often the ones who object the loudest about the drinking.

The enabler, however, in the final analysis, is the one who bails the alcoholic out when he gets into trouble. This is the one who pays the bail when the alcoholic is in jail, covers the checks when the account is overdrawn, lies to cover absenteeism, nurses him back to health when he is sick, and on we could go.

If you can convince this enabler to help get the alcoholic *into* trouble instead of *out of* trouble, you will be doing the greater service. To get the alcoholic out of trouble only prolongs the illness and assists him to an early demise.

The name of the game at this point is INTERVENTION. I am a firm believer in intervention into this uncontrolled behavior. If any significant in-roads are going to be made into this terrible illness, it will most likely be in this area of intervention. *When the symptoms of uncontrolled drinking arise* there should be intervention! This means that a person who is having a few, if any, problems in home, job, or worship might recognize that he cannot drink and just stop doing so at that point.

Today we are working primarily with the chronic alcoholics whose drinking has created some serious damage to their bodies, their families, their jobs, their social life, etc. Thus we need in-patient care where the deterioration is considerable, and the continuing care of A.A. for the vast majority of the rest. A decade ago the patients in our facilities were in their 50's, 60's, and 70's; today the averages have been lowered to the 30's, 40's and 50's. These younger people coming into treatment and into A.A. are not doing so because they are drinking earlier, but because we are intervening earlier into the illness.

When the Father in Jesus' parable let his son go he was, indeed, intervening into his alcoholic behavior. If he had followed him into the distant country and bailed him out every time he got into trouble, the story might never have ended as happily as it did. What this Father knew, and what each of us must learn before we become mature, responsible people, is that we have to be given the right to die before we are given the right to live; we have to be given the right to be sick before we are given the right to be well; we have to be given the right to stay drunk before we can be given the right to stay sober; we have to be given the right to go to hell before we can be given the right to go to heaven.

When I urge the enablers to let go of the alcoholic, I am only asking that they create this "crisis" so the value judgments can be made clear. If a person wants to die drinking there is really very little that anyone can do to change that determination. I believe, on the other hand, that when people are confronted with the opportunity to get well and function responsibly, the majority will choose that way.

Part of the illness of alcoholism is the inability to break out of the drinking pattern. Oftentimes the alcoholic, himself or herself, will cry for help and no one is listening. They will threaten suicide, or running away, or just say they aren't any good; and in most cases, these are cries for help. When you are mentally and physically preoccupied with a chemical, you aren't prone to ask to be taken away from it, thus the cries for help and outside intervention.

There is an old story about the man who bought a mule from his neighbor, but couldn't get the animal to go when he wanted it to; so he called over his neighbor and asked for his money back. The former owner picked up a 2 x 4 board, and hit the mule right between the ears. After this the mule obeyed every command it was given. The neighbor said to the man who had bought the mule, "First, you gotta get his attention!" So with the alcoholic— first, you have to get his attention!

There has been an old idea around for years that you must wait until the alcoholic reaches his bottom before you can do anything with him, or before he will respond to care. This is not true. The bottom will be different for every person and that bottom, or crisis, can be brought to bear long before it might have happened just by waiting for it to come to pass;

death, or something worse, could precede that particular moment you wait for.

To fail to intervene into this dreadful illness is the most merciless thing you can do. It is like standing by a railroad track watching a train go by, heading for a chasm where the bridge is out, and doing nothing whatsoever to stop the train. It is as though a physician, upon discovering a lump on a patient's body, just ignores it in the hope that it will go away or be easier to cure after it has become larger. We scoff at such thought, and yet that is exactly what we are doing when we fail to intervene where symptoms of alcoholism are present. I have seen entire communities and neighborhoods sit by passively while someone goes down the drain; they hope that this person will do something about his drinking.

It is at this point where the clergyman, the doctor, the lawyer, the law enforcement officer, the social worker, or anyone else who works with people's problems, can play an important role in recognition and intervention into alcoholism. When the clergyman sees the family problems, he *must* ask about drinking behavior. When the doctor sees nerves or other secondary effects of alcoholism, he should investigate drinking behavior. It is not necessary for the professional, be it a doctor or a lawyer, to be an authority on alcoholism; but rather, when he recognizes that this is a possibility in his client, it is important to refer him to the proper agency or individual.

There are any number of other ways that intervention can be carried out. Someone from outside of the family for whom the alcoholic has respect, can often walk in and say that something must be done; then make certain that it is done!

One of the earliest and easiest ways of seeking help is to take the alcoholic to a treatment facility when he is intoxicated. Just put him in the car; give him enough to keep him pretty well under, and then let him sober up in the detoxification unit of the hospital or treatment center.

Arrest can often be a good tool. If the person is arrested for driving while intoxicated, most judges would prefer to treat this person rather than punish him, especially when there has been no previous attempt to treat. Many an arrested alcoholic has found sobriety because a judge gave him the choice between 90 days in the workhouse or 21 days of alcoholism treatment. The treatment may not look any better than the workhouse at that point, but the 21 days of treatment certainly looks better than the 90 days in the workhouse. Many are the patients who walk into treatment centers with this choice hanging over their heads and inform the care center that they are there voluntarily.

Involuntary commitment to a public treatment center is a merciful act if the patient will not submit to any other help that is offered. I have come to the point where I'm not really concerned about the method used to get the chronic alcoholic into treatment, as long as he gets there. I have no qualms about coercing a patient into treatment when other ways fail, because it is difficult, if not impossible, to tell which patients do a better job of responding to treatment—those who walk in voluntarily or those who have been coerced.

While alcoholics are not saying it out loud, most tend to think they are the only one of their kind in existence. When forced into treatment and discover that the same crazy illness has afflicted others, they tend to back down and become very cooperative to treatment. I've heard some alcoholics resent those who coerced them into treatment, but it was only because they didn't want to quit. I have heard hundreds, on the other hand, who said, "Thank God some-one cared enough to get me the kind of help I needed!"

The wisest thing might be to close your ears to what the alcoholic has to say to you when you are coercing him into treatment; this is only part of the illness. Those who might need further proof of this would do well to sit at the entry door of any treatment facility and listen to the hostility that is often vented by the alcoholic when his chemical dependency is threatened. You can hear a lot before your ears fall off. When the alcoholic has been detoxified and treatment has been initiated, it is almost certain you will hear more thanks than reprisal.

Intervention simply means to me that the lunatics are through running the asylum, and the patient is no longer dictating the kind of care he will receive.

In this whole matter of intervention, I am also a believer in separation of husband and wife where one is an alcoholic, and things are going from bad to worse in the marriage and in the family. As I said earlier, the wife must choose to live with or without the husband if, indeed, he is the alcoholic, as there are few who can maintain any semblance of sanity while living with this behavior. Both suffer from a type of mental illness, and it isn't likely that in most cases anything constructive will be accomplished until they are separated from each other.

This separation can be accomplished through a voluntary separation, a legal separation, or a divorce action. Each must, of course, be dictated by its own circumstances. Only in relatively rare cases where it is unavoidable would I recommend this as a permanent separation or divorce, but rather as a step in the whole rehabilitation of the family.

We need in this family illness a legal instrument somewhere between separation and divorce that could keep two people apart long enough for each to get the kind of help necessary for their aspect of this illness. Voluntary separation is fine until one or the other changes his mind. Legal separation is often too detailed and expensive. Divorce carries with it a kind of finality that most tend to avoid until there is no hope of any other way. We must work with the legal instruments we do have which means that divorce must be used in some instances.

When divorce is discussed you occasionally hear the objection that the Bible says, "What therefore God has joined together, let no man put asunder." (Matthew 19:6—Jesus to the Pharisees) Others say that they are married "for better or worse," so will hang in there no matter what. I happen to believe very deeply in both of these injunctions, but where I see murder and suicide taking place on the installment basis in a family, I would much prefer to be guilty of promoting divorce rather than being a party to either of the former.

I, too, believe that what God has joined, man should not set aside, but where divorce seems to be the only way to "get the attention" of the afflicted party, I say it is worth the try. In most instances, the divorce will not come to pass because alcoholics love their wives, and when they discover they mean business about doing something to bring sanity back into the household, they will seek help.

I would also like to submit the fact here that in some of the marriages I deal with there is valid question whether God had anything to do with them. Marriage, to me, is the commitment of one life to another, under God, until death. I don't believe marriage starts at the altar, nor does it end in the divorce decree. The church can bless it, and the state can recognize it, but only God can bring it into being between the two parties involved.

Paul said, "Husbands, love your wives, as Christ loved the Church and gave himself up for her." (Ephesians 5:25) When a husband is willing, as Paul exorts, to lay his life down for his wife, I believe he is demonstrating his marriage commitment at its best. When I discover, however, that he is having difficulty deciding whether he wants to set a fifth of whiskey down for her, I have some question about the marriage. The story is told of the wife who, having had it up to here, set a fifth of whiskey on the table and said, "O.K. It's either the bottle or me!" To which the alcoholic responded by taking the bottle and telling her that next time she should give him a hard choice.

If a marriage was ever any good and the reason for marriage was valid, I believe it can always be brought back to something even better than it was originally by a rededication to a life of Godliness and to one another. Under these circumstances I would encourage a couple to mend their marriage when others might recommend that the divorce be carried out. At the same time, I question whether we are doing either party a favor by attempting to maintain something that did not, in fact, ever exist.

Another factor in what I consider to be the desirability of separation is the children in the family. The greatest security a child has, as far as I can gather, is two parents getting along together. The child has no money, he has no reputation to fall back on, he certainly believes in God but perhaps not in the utilitarian way He serves us. When a child looks to his parents and sees that everything is well in the castle, therein lies the child's greatest security.

When alcoholism enters the family picture, about the only thing the children can be sure of is that nothing is right between the parents and this does more to shatter their security than anything else imaginable.

In a family with two sick adults, someone must get his feet under him so he can salvage the children from greater damage than they have already received. In cases of separation, I have seen either the mother or the father alone do a marvelous job of re-establishing security for the children.

Many is the phony alcoholic who chides his family because he has given them plenty of food, clothing and shelter, when, in fact, the most important ingredients of love, compassion, and understanding have been missing. My heart has broken often over the suffering that innocent children have endured because of alcoholism in the family. If separation or divorce is necessary to turn that disaster about then, so be it; I stand quilty of being an advocate for divorce in these instances.

I can't forget some of the strongest words our Lord spoke on one occasion when He said, "But if a man is a cause of stumbling to one of these little ones who has faith in me, it would be better for him to have a millstone hung around his neck and be drowned in the depth of the sea."

There seems to be no indication that alcoholism is a hereditary illness, but it remains only natural that a child raised in the midst of unhealthy attitudes toward alcohol, together with the chaotic behavior of alcoholism, stands a much better than average chance of becoming an alcoholic also.

It is interesting to note in many instances where a decision to separate is made that the children will tend to want to go with the alcoholic spouse. When a wife, for instance, sues her alcoholic husband for legal separation or divorce, the children will often attempt to change the mother's mind. The reason for this is that the alcoholic parent will often attempt to buy the love of his children when he is coming off of a drunk. They remember his generosity when he is sober, and can't understand how their mother can hurt such a wonderful man.

On the other hand, the mother has often been the only one to discipline the children in the absence of the father, and the children, not realizing the conflicts the mother is under, cannot understand why she is so short tempered and intolerant at times. A child cannot be expected to understand the dynamics of a marriage, and, therefore, when separation or divorce seems to be the best way to go, it ought to be done over any objections that children may make. This, of course, is only one of the great tragedies that weave themselves in and out of the entire alcoholic drama.

It should be made clear too that if the non-alcoholic wife or husband chooses to let go of his spouse in separation or divorce in hopes of making intervention into the alcoholic behavior, then he must face the reality that he may never get him back or see him again. When the Father in the parable let his son go, he certainly had no guarantee that he would ever get him back. This is precisely what "letting go" means. I liken this to standing on a dock, cutting a rope that holds the boat, and then pushing it out. Now, for the first time in a long time, the alcoholic must make some decisions; the major one being whether he quits drinking and regains his family and home life, or whether he continues drinking and loses his loved ones, and dies.

Part of alcoholic behavior is to keep the pressure of blame on the spouse which automatically demands that she must make decision after decision; then, whatever decision is made, it is called wrong and blame is applied.

I like to see a crisis created where the alcoholic must now come to the cross-road and make the most important decision of his life. I believe that in the overwhelming number of instances he will choose sobriety and return to the family. The sooner that decision is demanded, the more apt the story is to have a happy ending.

One must know the end of the story in our parable before he can fully understand why the Father let his son go. If he had chased after his alcoholic son like wives and parents chase after their alcoholic spouses and children, he would only have become all the more sick himself. Besides, it seems to be true that the closer you are to the chronic alcoholic, the less you can do to talk sense with him. This is often why an A.A. member, or some other total stranger, can walk into an alcoholic family situation and get some healing activity started that the family by itself has been unable to initiate.

There is a kind of paralysis around this illness; everyone hopes that tomorrow will be better, but it just doesn't happen that way with an illness that becomes progressively worse. We might think that if a person stops drinking for a period of time, that were he to continue, he would begin where he left off. But, this is not the case! The progressive nature of this illness is such that his drinking would progress as though he had been drinking during the entire period of abstinence.

The spouse, by letting the alcoholic go, and

then getting her own house in order by going to Alanon, church, and professional help, where necessary, will maintain physical, mental, and spiritual health so that if or when the arrested alcoholic returns, he will be accepted as the Father in our parable was able to receive his son. It is difficult to love the unlovely, but this is exactly what the spouse must do when her sober husband returns after what may have been years of destructive behavior.

In a relatively short time, the alcoholic can return to what we might think of as normal behavior, but the illness of the non-alcoholic spouse may take years to level out. If there have been years of drinking, and perhaps infidelity along with it, how long does it take before trust can be restored? How long does it take his wife, for instance, who has been wrung out emotionally to return to some semblance of her normal self? Longer, I tend to think, than anyone realizes!

Along these lines, I like to remind each patient who is leaving treatment and returning to his family, that he is going back to a household of sick people. When he arrives home, detoxified and in apparent good health, it may create more resentment from the spouse and children who may have found no help. Their inability to receive him back as he would like is only a part of the debris left from his drinking experience. I urge each one leaving treatment facilities to be as patient as possible with the

"Stay-at-homes," and perhaps demonstrate the same kind of patience for them now in some difficult days that they must have shown him during the early days of his chronic drinking behavior.

When you consider how sick the people are back home, it is really miraculous that as many alcoholics remain sober as do on returning home. This points up the need for family counseling while the patient is in treatment. More and more we are seeing, and will see in the future, the entire family being treated. If alcoholism is a galaxy illness in nature, it is only reasonable that the various parts of this galaxy be treated and helped in a way that will meet their need.

There is an old saying in A.A. "Let Go—Let God." While it is intended to describe one's relationship to God, I think it might also be used here where we talk about the spouse's letting go when it seems that all other attempts fail. It is at this point that Alanon can play a very significant role, and a place, too, where the clergyman can play a very supportive role for both parties in an extremely difficult period in their illness.

I have stood by the caskets and preached funeral sermons for alcoholics where no meaningful intervention was carried out. On the other hand, I am welcome in many homes today as a friend where I assisted in meaningful intervention, even divorce, but where they are together again and enjoying a happiness that supersedes anything they had ever known in the past.

When we concern ourselves with the alcoholic, for whatever reason, we must never forget the "Stay-at-Homes."

Chapter III

The Tragedy of Abundance

Alcoholism is "The Tragedy of Abundance." We have no reason to believe that the young man in Jesus' parable enjoyed anything but the best of circumstances. Apparently it was a fine household in which he was raised; he enjoyed all the comforts of home: a comfortable house, good food, clean beds, loving parents, and everything else we feel goes into a good home.

This young man was undoubtedly quite a gregarious person; he had a good personality and a clever mind. The work he did, he did well, even to the point of perfection. While he was probably an impetuous rascal, we can imagine that deep down he was the "apple of his Father's eye," and if we had to be around either of the sons, we would likely choose the younger over the elder. In these respects, he was typically the alcoholic personality.

An earmark of his alcoholism is seen in the words of the parable, "A few days later the younger son turned the whole of his share into CASH and left home for a distant country.'' If there is anything similar in every alcoholic, it is the need for cash. Needless to say, it is an expensive activity; for when the alcoholic has crossed the threshhold into alcohol dependence, or in fact a drug dependency, when he needs a drink, he needs a drink!

At this point he isn't drinking because he wants to drink; he is drinking because he has to drink. Cash looks good to the alcoholic because it means that when he needs a drink he has the where-with-all to get it. Cash means that he can get what his body, mentally and physically, craves. After all, when you need a drink, what good are five shares of AT&T, or the deed to the house? What he needs is legal tender to get what he needs most at that particular time—alcohol.

Alcoholics, who by nature seem to be extremely honest, will turn around and cash a bad check to get something to drink. I could guarantee that 99 out of 100 alcoholics wouldn't take five cents that was not theirs, but would turn around and cash bad checks, steal from their kids' piggy bank, sell the spare tire, and pull every kind of financial manipulation possible to get the money when they need a drink.

These are the same people who will lie verbally when it is easier to tell the truth. It will do little good in most of these cases to lecture on honesty and integrity until the person is withdrawn from the chemical, and then the need to lecture in most cases will be gone.

Certainly there is dishonesty in every one of us; this is but the fractured image of God in each of us. When I am dealing with alcoholics and I see this dishonesty, I like to believe that they are primarily alcoholic and secondarily thieves, adulterers, fighters, etc.

What we are secondarily or what we are when we are intoxicated is something that no one should find out. If for no other reason, this is why intoxication or drunkenness should be abhored in each of us individually and in our society as well. In those segments of our society where alcohol is used and yet remains a minimum problem factor, you will discover that drunkenness is not a tolerated behavior. The best case in point is the conservative Jewish community where alcohol is used often in meaningful ways, but drunkenness is frowned upon.

In the orthodox Jewish family the children are introduced early in a meaningful way to the use of wine. On Friday evening at sundown when the Sabbath begins, the mother pours the wine for the children as well as the adults as they celebrate the Sabbath meal. It is apparent that in those segments of society where children are introduced early, in a meaningful way, to the use of alcohol, they tend less to abuse it later. Whenever drunkenness is frowned upon and considered to be unacceptable behavior, there is also a marked tendency to be less abusive of beverage alcohol. This is a definite feeling among the orthodox Jewish community.

Alcoholics like to tuck a five, ten, twenty, or one-hundred dollar bill up under the flap of their billfold to insure against an emergency when they lack funds to buy booze. How many wives have admitted that they didn't know their husbands were paid twice a month, or held an extra job, or got a year-end bonus and used it for drinking money? When you have a harmful dependence on alcohol, make no mistake about the fact that the first dollars go for alcohol, and what is left goes to the family for esssential bills.

This "money-to-drink" factor points up the need for industries' involvement in the whole identification and intervention aspect of alcoholism. Alcoholism has been called "Industries' Two Billion Dollar Hangover." When you consider all the absenteeism, wasted time, mistakes, bad deals, etc., you can imagine that the two billion is a minimum figure.

Because of the need for money to perpetuate the alcohol dependency, the alcoholic will do everything to protect his job. Strangely enough, in many instances, everything else has deteriorated, but the job still gets done. Here, too, the wife lies about his absences and failures because, even though she may be getting only a portion of the check he brings home, it is still better than being on the welfare roles.

Industry can intervene here in a meaningful way and hit or threaten the alcoholic where it will hurt him the most—in the pocketbook. Historically, industry has turned its head to the drinking behavior of the alcoholic employee until it got so bad that the only alternative was to fire him. This is tragic and unnecessary. More often than not, the sober alcoholic is the best employee they have; to fire him means a loss for all parties involved.

Every employer, be they public or private, ought to have a policy for the illness alcoholism like he does for other illnesses and provision to provide care when it is detected. A growing number of corporations are beginning to incorporate this kind of policy into their personnel benefits. When personnel supervisors note absenteeism or intoxication on the job, they should have the right to grant this person a leave of absence to receive the kind of treatment needed. This does not apply only to the laborer or the blue collar employee, but to management as well. There is just as much alcoholism, if not more, in management as there is anywhere else in the various strata of industry. Often, too, when there is alcoholism at the management level, there will be a defensiveness toward the subject and a hesitancy to establish a good policy regarding it among the employees.

Many an employer, who has hired the

arrested alcoholic or helped him to sobriety while keeping him on the pay roll, will confide that it is like getting two employees back for the price of one, referring to the alcoholic's integrity and capability as a worker.

Industry need not feel that its need to intervene and help the alcoholic employee back to health is entirely a philanthropic venture. It is, in fact, just good business. Most businesses have many dollars invested in every employee and know how costly it is to hire and train new people. A few dollars spent to identify the alcoholic employee early and get him to proper care will sweeten the profit column for the company which in turn will make the stockholders happy.

Our parable tells us that when the young man had turned his securities into cash, he left for the distant country where he squandered his new-formed fortune in reckless living. We can well imagine what was included in that reckless living. We see it about us everyday in the lives of alcoholics and non-alcoholics alike.

It might be well to stop and take note here that all of the reckless living he was doing was being done on "borrowed" capital. The money he had received was not earned, but came to him only as the result of his birth. In this respect each of us should stop and examine our own lives. How often do we stop to realize that the air we breathe, the heart that beats within us, and all the good things that come into our lives are an inheritance from our Father? How often do we take for granted all these things we enjoy and fail to realize that they have come to us only as the result of our Father's goodness.

In my listening to the Fifth Step of alcoholics over the years where they "Admitted to God, to ourselves, and to another human being, the exact nature of our wrongs" (Fifth Step Alcoholics Anonymous), I found that nothing bothers alcoholics more as they look back over their lives than the waste of time, talent, and material things while they were drinking. They realize they were created for better things and that they hadn't made the most of the opportunities that were theirs.

The waste of human talent from alcoholism is beyond our comprehension. Many lives have passed from the scene prematurely because of alcoholism; others have only existed while they lived; and all of them had great talent and could have made a considerable contribution to the welfare of man had they received help and been restored to health and dignity. We can ill afford this loss of human resource in this or any age.

As you may have guessed, I believe that alcoholics are gifted people. I think alcoholism is the illness of gifted people, and one of the reasons we call it the "Tragedy of Abundance." It afflicts most frequently the gifted in our society. I believe this to the extent that when I am talking to someone to determine in my own mind if he is an alcoholic, I question whether he is if I sense a dullness, and am somewhat aware that there is no brain damage.

Some of the most brillant people I have come to know over the years are alcoholics. From the time when I was a child I can remember my parents and other adults shaking their heads and talking about someone who had a drinking problem. Invariably they would say that when he was sober, he was the best farmer around, the best doctor, the best teacher, the best clergyman, the best neighbor and friend you could have —WHEN HE WAS SOBER! When he was drinking, it was another story. I am sure that you could take ten people from any walk of life, and if one of the ten was an alcoholic, he or she would be equal or superior to any of his peers. Truly we are confronted here with the "Tragedy of Abundance."

I have often likened our society today to a colossal alcoholic; we seem in most every situation to be able to handle our difficulties and adversities better than we do our prosperity and affluence. I tend to be more fearful of an alcoholic's going back to drinking during his good times than during his times of trial. The alcoholic is more apt to drink following a raise in pay than after being fired, all other factors being equal.

We are reminded from time to time that we can destroy ourselves, as a nation, from within even more effectively than we can by any outside threat. This is an alcoholic kind of reality. There is no substitute for Godly living to prevent alcoholic behavior at any level, and there is no better therapy than Godly living to restore one if there has been a deterioration or fall.

Now, if I believe that all alcoholics are gifted persons, I also believe that they are equally immature. The young man in Jesus' parable was immature. He thought that "things" could make him happy and enable him to enjoy life. What he failed to understand, and what so many of us fail to understand, is that "things" just don't have the capacity to give us the peace of mind and internal joy that we need for effective living. We need money, good food and drink, clothes, shelter, reputation, self-respect and all the rest, but we must never ask these "things" to give us what only God can give. We are creatures of God and, therefore, only God can give us that happiness which we all covet for ourselves. If we were the creation of General Electric or General Motors, "things" would make us happy. But we aren't their creation; therefore, we must find our peace and joy in the Father's household and then let all the rest of these "things" take their proper relationship to Him.

When the young man in the parable left home, he entered a corridor that would ultimately lead to destruction because it was a life with God left out. God does not command us in the first commandment, "You shall have no other gods before Me," nor does Christ exhort us in Matthew 6:33 to "Seek first his kingdom and his righteousness, and all these things shall be yours as well," because God is some kind of an egotist. He does so because if He isn't first, everything else will be out of place. It is like buttoning your shirt: if you get the first button wrong, it will be wrong all the way. So it is when God does not occupy the chief seat in our hearts.

In the Sermon on the Mount when Jesus said to seek first his kingdom, I think he made it clear that all these other things that gain our attention are not necessarily evil in themselves, but first must come first.

When we ask "things" to satisfy us, we will ultimately pervert them and they will turn around to destroy us. My friend who said to me concerning alcohol, "My best friend betrayed me," was merely saying that alcohol did what he asked it to do until that day when the drink took the man and nearly destroyed his life before he found sobriety in A.A. When the reward of alcohol euphoria was replaced by the punishment that overwhelms the alcohol-dependent person, he can only conclude that this "best friend" now threatens every area of his existence.

Maturity is a difficult state of being to define. Any number of definitions would be correct. Maturity to me, however, means the development of many kinds of responses to the various problems and challenges of life, and then application of the best response to a given situation. This means that in any given situation there is a time to yell, lose your temper, hold your temper, pray, get angry, be tolerant, be intolerant, smile, cry, go for a walk, run away, stay and fight, and on and on we can go. Immaturity would be the opposite of this: a person responds in only one way to everything that comes along. A child will lie on the floor and have a tantrum; the alcoholic says, "I'll show you. I'll get drunk."

The immaturity of the alcoholic can be seen in his slowly solving every problem and situation by going to the bottle. When he arrives at the chronic stage of his drinking, he is drinking health, God, and everything else out of the bottle. I had an alcoholic tell me one time that in alcohol he found a god who responded right now to his needs. No one can deny that there was an element of truth in what he said, but there were better ways of meeting those needs without ultimately destroying himself. I've likened this to the downspout on a house: the rain falls all over the roof but runs to the edge and then into the gutter and then over to the downspout and down. So, in the same sense, the alcoholic runs into all the problems of life, and a few more because of his drinking. But instead of standing firm and responding to each in kind, he goes to the bottle like rain to the downspout and tries to solve all of them out of the bottle.

The no-small task of the treatment facility, A.A., the church, and anyone else who gets into the picture, is to turn this person around and establish him in a new way of life, a new orientation to problem solving, and to help him learn to live comfortably with reality, without alcohol.

The most difficult of the Twelve Steps of A.A. is the first one where it says, "We admitted we were *powerless* over alcohol—that our lives had become unmanageable." We have been talking about the alcoholic as a gifted person. Certainly we could equate this gifted person to a powerful person. It is hard for a powerful person to admit he is powerless in any area of his life.

The alcoholic is often one who has built some sort of dynasty in which he functions. He has manipulated people and organizations. There just aren't many situations that come along that he can't handle. Personality-wise, he can "woo a bird off of a branch." Some of the acting the alcoholic does when he is trying to work his way back into the family or into the job which has been threatened would be worthy of an academy award. For this powerful, capable person to admit that he is powerless over alcohol is really the big hurdle in his total recovery.

This is not an illness that he can intellectualize his way out of. I have seen some very brilliant people attempt to do so and fail miserably. Many alcoholics, who are filled with remorse in the morning, vow never to take another drink, but by 10:00 the same morning are back at it.

These vows, made countless times by drinking alcoholics, are remindful of St. Paul's words to the Christians in Rome when he said, "For I do not do the good I want, but the evil I do not want is what I do." (Romans 7:19) This statement of Paul's has often caused me to wonder if the thorn he speaks of in II Corinthians 12:7, "a thorn was given me in the flesh," might not have been alcoholism. His early life and later insights into his inner self could certainly identify him as an alcoholic personality. The answer to that question must wait until that Last Day when all the hidden secrets of the universe will be revealed.

The young man of whom Jesus speaks was slowly, but surely, exchanging his abundant endowment of money into chaos and tragedy. He was running the whole gammit of "Wine, Women and Song." As an alcoholic, he was demonstrating the grandiose behavior so familiar to this illness. He would typically "belly up" to the bar and set up drinks for the house. When he drank, everyone drank!

How many alcoholics have bought drinks for the house when the rent wasn't paid and there wasn't enough food and clothing for the children at home? The alcoholic has the Satanic capacity of befriending a total stranger and then going home to tongue-lash the people who love and serve him.

Certainly the word filtered back to the "Stay-at-homes" in the parable, because when the Prodigal did come back, the elder brother objected to accepting him. He noted: "But now that this son of yours turns up, after running through your money with his women . . ." It had broken the heart of the Father when he heard how his son was behaving, but he had let him go and now all he could do was pray that something might happen to turn him around.

Well, it happened! He ran out of money and for him, like for so many alcoholics, it was a blessing in disguise. There are many alcoholics who are sober today because they ran out of money and, as a result, were forced in one way or another into help. There are also many alcoholics who are dead today because they didn't run out of money and drank themselves to death. The young man in our text ran out of money, and when he ran out of money he also ran out of friends—the bar-flies who hang on as long as someone else buys. Besides all that, a famine came upon that country and everyone was apparently hard put for the necessities of life.

Here is our young friend: broke, sick, hungry, needing a drink to get well, homeless, friendless, rejected! This isn't what he had planned for himself and yet this is where all of

the running from God
the fear of looking inside
the fear of tomorrow
the fear of death
the fear of living
the lost hours and days from blackouts
the lonesomeness
the waste of time

How do you explain the helplessness and despair of being sick and tired of being sick and tired? You are sick and tired physically; you are sick and tired mentally; you are sick and tired Spiritually; you are sick and tired morally; you are sick and tired socially. Figure it anyway you like, but it all adds up to being sick and tired of being sick and tired.

The young man in our parable ends up living with, and being a servant to, a herd of pigs. He had never planned it that way, nor had he ever dreamt that he would arrive at this way back there when he was enjoying his days of affluence and abundance. Nevertheless, he ends up with the pigs!

To say that he was a pig would demand an apology to the pigs, for there are things that pigs would never think of doing that people do when left to themselves and their base passions. It has been said that man is the only being who eats when he is full and breeds out of season.

We are not punished *for* our sins as much as *by* our sins. How often has God been visualized as one who keeps track of our sins while we wait for the ax to fall. If God punished us for our sins he would have wiped us all off the face of the earth a long time ago. The young man in our text was suffering what he did not because someone else had inflicted it upon him, but rather as a result of his own doing.

When the writer of Proverbs says, "The way of the faithless is their ruin" (Proverbs 13:15b), he is not talking about God's punishment as much as about the transgressor's hurting of himself. As we look about in the world and see the hurt and suffering among men, it cannot be thought of as God's punishment, but rather as man's inhumanity to himself and his fellow man.

The reason God has given us the Ten Commandments and the other directives of His Word is not because He doesn't want us to have fun and enjoy ourselves, but because he knows that unless we obey His rules we will indeed hurt ourselves. What hurts us hurts Him. When parents lay down rules for their children to obey, they don't do so in order to have reason to punish them but to avoid the hurt that may come to them if they do not live by the rules. It is the loving will of God that no one be hurt; but man, in his rebellion, finds this difficult to perceive. The Father's heart breaks when the younger son leaves home because he knows of the hurt that can befall his son when he leaves the sphere of parental love and protection.

What we witness in the young man's descent

and ultimate arrival in the pig pen is man's normal inclination apart from God. We call this rebelliousness; we call it sin. But, I think a better word for our day would be phoniness. Every person is a phony! All this says is that we are not God, who is genuine. Out of our phoniness can come all kinds of deviant behavior.

Too often, I think, we envision sin as a wrongful act, when that is just the tip of the iceberg in our lives of phoniness. Phoniness carries with it more of the corruption of our entire nature rather than a mistake we may make from day to day in our lives. If Jesus spoke to us today, he would say, "I have come not to call the righteous but sinners (phonies) to repentance." (Matthew 9:13)

One of the really great tragedies of alcoholism is that, because of this uncontrolled behavior around alcohol, the alcoholic demonstrates a kind of behavior that he or she might never have shown were it not for his drinking. If you took any number of the finest Godly people imaginable and they become intoxicated, you would discover them exhibiting behavior not unlike any alcoholic or other intoxicated person.

It breaks my heart to visit prisoners in our penal institutions who are there because they have committed crimes while intoxicated, or perhaps even during blackouts that are a part of alcoholism. When you visit with alcoholic prisoners, you discover that they are just as

63

good as anyone else, and if it weren't for their illness they would be enjoying freedom with their families and friends.

I fear that, too often, those of us within the framework of the Christian Church leave the impression that Christianity is goodness, when, in fact, it isn't. If this is our concept of Christianity, then we will go around trying to impress people with how good we are and how much God has done to make us good people. Naturally, the alcoholic, who may have pulled every trick in the book, isn't going to get too close to this kind of an organization because he hasn't had too much going for him in the goodness ledger while involved in alcoholic behavior.

The only thing that any one of us has to offer to God that is peculiar to ourselves is sin and phoniness. All else is His! All the rest is only to be used, cared for, and managed while here on earth. When we bring our offerings to God, the first one we must bring is our sin. When we do so, we are assured by the Apostle John in his first letter: "If we confess our sins, he is faithful and just, and will forgive our sins and cleanse us from all unrighteousness." (I John 1:9)

I heard an alcoholism counselor tell one time of a man who had been in treatment for alcoholism and, upon release, went back to church as he had been encouraged to do. When he arrived at the entrance to the church, however, he overheard some do-gooder in the parish remark, "What's that damn drunk doing here?"

Some weeks later this alcoholic committed suicide. It is evident that the parishioner who made such a statement wouldn't know a Christian if he tripped over one. God have mercy on us if, either by such word or action, we ever leave such an impression upon those who come to the church for the healing of Christ, regardless of their sin-sickness.

Christianity is a way of life that results from the confluence of man's weakness with the strength and power of God. He comes to us in our weakness and reconciles us to Himself through the redemptive activity of our Brother, Jesus Christ. Whatever righteousness I may possess, whatever holiness, whatever goodness is not really mine at all, but that which has been reflected through me by faith in Jesus Christ.

Growth in holiness, therefore, is not growth in goodness but growth in dependence upon Christ. If I boast of my goodness or attempt to exhibit it among men, I am only demonstrating my phoniness. Whenever we run into someone trying to impress us with his goodness, it is time to be careful because we are in the presence of a phony to end all phonies. The Apostle Paul in his second letter to the Christians in Corinth said, "For it is not the man who commends himself that is accepted, but the man whom the Lord commends." (II Corinthians 10:18)

Within each of us lies every seed of sin known to mankind. This means that if any one of us is lonesome enough, broke enough, drunk enough, sick enough, afraid enough, hurt enough, mad enough, he is capable of committing any sin in the book. When we see an alcoholic, therefore, or anyone else who has fallen in one way or another, we have no right to think of him as being different from ourselves, for we would have done exactly as he has done if we were that person.

It is at this point that Alcoholics Anonymous took a page from the Christian faith which is one of the keys to its success. When A.A. demands "the admittance of powerlessness" upon entry into the fellowship, it is reflecting the very best of Christianity. All the great people of God have been those who were aware of their weakness.

When David in Psalm 51 says, "For I know my transgressions, and my sin is ever before me. Against thee, thee only, have I sinned, and done that which is evil in thy sight" (Psalm 51: 3,4), he isn't talking about his strength. He was a man who knew his phoniness to the extent of adultery and murder. His ultimate greatness grew out of his weakness.

When St. Paul cries out, "Wretched man that I am! Who will deliver me from this body of death? (Romans 7:24) he isn't verbalizing his strengths; he is betraying his weakness. Paul gives us the key when he says the Lord said to him, "My grace is sufficient for you, for my power is made perfect in weakness." (II Corinthians 12:9) Then Paul concedes, "For when I am weak, then I am strong." (II Corinthians 12:10b)

We can be too strong for God to work with and through; but we can never be too weak. It is only as we admit our weakness that we become the kind of instruments through which He can play and bring about his will in the lives of men.

This precept of our weakness really being our strength is hard to accept, just like the difficulty the alcoholic has when this powerful person must admit he is powerless. But when we think of it, the greatest relationships that we have are built on weakness. If you will stop and think of the closest friend you have on earth, I think you will discover that that person knows more about your weaknesses than anyone else. What is a good friend but one with whom we can be ourselves and share our weaknesses.

This certainly holds true of marriage as well. The better the marriage the more you can be assured that both parties have betrayed their weaknesses to one another. Divorce is the result of two strong people assuring one another that they can get along quite well without the other. Come along, however, to the Fiftieth Wedding Anniversary, and see the couple who has lived their years together. They know each other's weaknesses very well, but their love is greater and overlooks the weaknesses. If you could get deep down into the hearts of these two people, there would be a little voice that says, "I can't live without you." Thus you see the heartbreak and lonesomeness when one or the other is taken. Often the survivor does not live too long because he hasn't the mate to lean on.

Two people leaning on one another is the strongest thing in the world. When one alcoholic admits he is powerless and leans on another who admits he is powerless, they have the strongest relationship in the world. They are demonstrating the power of God. Everyone needs this kind of relationship to a friend whether he is alcoholic or not.

What we discover in this whole concept of two weak people leaning on one another begetting strength is that ordinary people do a better job of healing one another than all the professionals put together. Personally, I believe that 90% of the healing that takes place in an alcoholic treatment facility is carried on between the patients themselves; the remaining 10% is the result of the professional therapists on the staff. I also believe that the in-patient treatment part of the therapy is only about 10% of the total recovery process, while the 90% balance takes place after the patient has returned home and is involved in an ongoing, out-patient, peer-group treatment, like A.A. I cannot prove my statistics, to be sure, but I use them to point out what I consider the importance of this whole "strength through weakness" concept.

I have an idea that this is exactly what God had intended the Christian concept of the Communion of Saints to be, but we tended to feel that it was too simple and abandoned it back there somewhere for something more complex and theological.

Maybe one of these days we will discover that if God is anything, He is considerably more practical than he is theological. We like to get involved in theological jargon and then Jesus comes to us and says that the way we treat one another as human beings is exactly the way we treat Him. We can talk about how much we love God until we are blue in the face, but in the final analysis, what we think about God will be borne out in our everyday treatment of one another. The Apostle John summed it up well in his first letter when he said, "For he who does not love his brother whom he has seen, cannot love God whom he has not seen." (I John 4:20b)

The whole thrust of Christianity is that God has indentified Himself in the Human Form of Jesus Christ. Jesus is the Incarnation or God in the flesh. In His human form he has redeemed me by way of the cross and now remains the window through which I look to discover more about Him and His will for my life. In yet another sense, Christ is incarnate in every human being. By becoming human He has added dignity to human life. Whenever and wherever we discover human suffering, we must do what we can to end it for there is no better way of honoring God than to help our brother in need. The alcoholic is no exception to this.

Before we leave this chapter on being sick and tired of being sick and tired, we ought to look at a behavior that is common to acoholism. It is what is known as *Rationalization*. Rationalization is the use of illogical reasoning to support unreasonable behavior. Few areas of alcoholic behavior do a better job of describing inherent phoniness than does rationalization.

When a person begins to drink he may do so for all kinds of reasons. We may agree or disagree that they are valid reasons, but nevertheless they are reasons.

The alcoholic, however, discovers somewhere along the line that his drinking is different from that of his peers, so he tends to compensate by rationalizing his behavior. When the alcoholic crosses the threshold into a mental and physical preoccupation with ethyl alcohol, he also leaves behind all valid reasons for drinking.

There may have been reasons for drinking at one time, but that time has now passed. In other words, he has no problems now that drinking is going to help. Just because you may be nuts, however, does not mean you are crazy, so the alcoholic must maintain some kind of rationale around his drinking.

It is at this point that he may say, among other things, "Who wouldn't drink with a wife like mine . . . a back like mine . . . a job like mine . . . a boss like mine?" or all the other fabrications one might think up.

If the wife says, "Good morning!" he says she is mouthing off. If she doesn't, he accuses her of the silent treatment. The end result is a *reason*, however slim, to go out and get back to the drinking.

The wife of the periodic alcoholic can set either her watch or the calendar by the illogical reasoning the husband becomes involved in before he begins to drink again.

It is in this area of rationalization that those who work with the alcoholic would do well to turn off their hearing aids. When you have long since left all reasons for drinking behind, it is of little value to listen to all the reasons why he or she continues to do so. Rationalization is nothing but the vastness of the subconscious mind calling out to get back to the chemical dependency it has been taught to adapt to over the years. Alcoholics must be helped to examine every attitude and conduct to make sure that behind it or through it they are not preparing to drink. This can include something as complex as a trip to Italy where wine would be served with the meal, or as simple as getting into a group or a frame of reference right at home where earlier drinking is the vogue.

If the genius that is used by alcoholics to continue drinking were ever gathered together and harnessed for good, I have no doubt whatsoever that we could solve in a matter of days the great problems of war, disease, pollution, etc., that confront our civilization today. When this genius is exerted, however, to maintain the chronic illness of alcoholism there comes a time when you just plain get sick and tired of being sick and tired.

Chapter V

The Miracle of Memory

We have followed the young man of Jesus'
parable through his alcoholic decline from the
security of the Father's household, through the
days of reckless living, to the end of that corridor which leads to destruction. There he lies
between two sows, trying to gain a little warmth
against the cool night air. The shirt with the
Bunny cuff links, which was only days before, it
seemed, the symbol of his "class," is now torn
and filthy. Jesus says that at this point, "No one
gave him anything." (Luke 15:16b)

This fellow who had been given so much in
love, ability, prosperity, personality, and all the
rest is getting nothing from anyone.

He is alone! He is friendless! He is, as we said
in the last chapter, sick and tired of being sick
and tired! He has had it!

But now as he reaches his extremity, as so often happens with the alcoholic, something happened. The words of the parable simply say,
"But when he came to himself." (Luke 15:17a)
As he lies there in that filth and despair, his

mind travels back over the days and years and comes to rest at his Father's home. He had been so busy up to now just having a good time for himself, and then trying to prevent disaster, and then just trying to keep body and soul together that he really hadn't taken time to think about home. But think about home he did, and Jesus says that he reminded himself, "How many of my father's hired servants have bread enough and to spare, but I perish here with hunger! I will arise and go to my father, and I will say to him, 'Father, I have sinned against heaven and before you; I am no longer worthy to be called your son; treat me as one of your hired servants.' " (Luke 15:17-19)

When we first met this young man in the parable he was sick of home. Now a miracle has taken place! His attitude has changed. He suffers from yet another illness, HOMESICKNESS!

Homesickness is a strange illness; it really hurts, but it is also a good illness because the entire dilemma is a tribute to home. Many a soldier and sailor has dreamt of home and how good it would be to pull up around that table with Mom and Dad and the rest of the family. If he closes his eyes he can smell the beef roast, and the fresh bread, and all the other wonderful smells of a good home.

All this went through our young friend's head and, finally when he could stand it no longer, he got to his feet, brushed himself off and took off for home. What a sight that was as he lifted himself over the fence and headed for home!

Whatever caused him to turn the corner? Whatever possessed him to get up and head for home? Was it the filth of the pig pen? Never! What was it then? It was a memory—the miracle of memory!

What is it that causes alcoholics to pick themselves up and go back to the kind of life they were created to live? What is it that makes them vow they will now seek and do whatever they must do in order to find sobriety? Is it the rotten life? No, it isn't the rotten life that turns them around any more than it was the pig pen that turned the young man in the parable around.

Alcoholics quit drinking for the same reason the young man headed for home—because of the miracle of memory!

You can't help the alcoholic by threatening him with hell, death, or any other unpleasant ultimatum. After all, how can you go to hell when, in fact, you have been there in reality through all the years of alcoholism?

What more terrible tribute to God is there than to attempt to win people for Him by threatening those who don't want Him that they will go to hell? That's like a young man asking his girl to marry him and, if she doesn't, threatening to kill her.

The person experiencing the hell of chronic

alcoholism needs the treat of more hell to change him like he needs another hole in the head.

I can't say that I can ever recollect anyone who went to heaven because he was afraid of hell. The people who say they love God and go to church because they don't want to go to hell are only making some kind of deal for hell insurance, and it is a waste of time. The person who wants to quit drinking only because he doesn't want to die drunk isn't on very good footing either.

The sickest alcoholic, along with those suffering from some other forms of illnesses, will turn the corner and begin to get well when someone is around who will arouse his memory to the fact that he is the object of God's love. The overwhelming majority of alcoholics were taught this in their homes and churches, but have forgotten. The old hymn said it, "I heard the voice of Jesus say, 'Come unto me and rest.'" It is the call of a loving God that changes the lives of men.

There is some of God in every man, and He calls that part to Himself and builds on that part of God within himself. Isn't a good teacher one who calls out the intelligence in a person? You don't just load a student down with facts; you draw out from him that miracle of intelligence. Isn't a good physician one who draws and builds on the health of an individual while he attacks the disease? Isn't the best soul winner that one who can call out the finest and best in the life of another?

In over a decade of listening to alcoholics pour out their hearts in the Fifth Step and otherwise, I find it isn't the filth that bothers them the most—it's the failure to live up to their abilities and potentialities. They regret not having taken advantage of their opportunities. They know they were created for better things. All this is memory—a miraculous memory that calls them back to a life with God.

I have asked countless alcoholics what the first song was that they ever learned. Many have answered, "Jesus Loves Me, This I Know." What's wrong with that memory? If you know that Jesus loves you there is a memory that can turn your life around.

How can we convince the alcoholics that they are the objects of God's love and concern? The answer lies in becoming involved in their lives and doing what we can in a meaningful way to intervene into the alcoholic pattern. When clergymen ask me what they should say to the alcoholic, I like to respond. "Tell him anything you want. He is so fouled up you can't make it much worse; but above all, get involved in that life." I know of no way you can teach people how to work with anyone until they get involved in a number of lives and make all the mistakes it is possible to make and experience the success that provides momentum to continue.

We tend to live in a "gutless" era where love

is equated with passivity: turning our heads and ignoring the problems of people. "Why bother?" is the familiar refrain. When you get involved and risk your reputation, and all the rest, in an attempt to get someone to treatment, the word comes through to that person loud and clear, "Here is someone who cares for me!" It's O.K. to care, and everyone who has the welfare of his fellowman at heart will expend himself attempting to find ways in which he can be the kind of conductor through which God can carry out His healing in the lives of people.

If we are the people of God, there must be an optimism and enthusiasm for healing. If we really believe that God is alive and that He is Life and Health, then we must reflect Him however we can.

One might write volumes about that moment in the lives of alcoholics when they decided to do something about their drinking. Some of the stories are heart-rending and others are hilarious.

One man told me some time ago that he was sitting on the back steps of his home trying to come out of a hangover when his little girl came up to him, slid her arm around and over his, and just said, "Daddy, don't drink any more." To my knowledge, he hasn't had a drink since! Call it what you want. That little girl who loved her daddy intervened, and it probably meant more than all the professional advice that might have been offered.

One I shall never forget is the man who lost several fine jobs through drinking. After several trips to a treatment center, we convinced the wife she should get out. After she left, nothing happened. He continued drinking! It was as if nothing had happened; the sought-after crisis didn't arise.

Finally, when we had closed off all his income and literally isolated him from everything, he had to go to a half-way house to live. (A half-way house is a temporary residence for homeless men or women.)

All through the drinking years there had been this large white cat. It had been cared for and loved by this man for years. Before he left for the half-way house, he took his cat to the veterinarian to be put away because he would no longer be able to care for it. He told me later that as he left the veterinarian's office and walked to his car that he said to himself, "What the hell! I can't even keep a cat alive!" That man hasn't had a drink since that day over five years ago. Today he has an excellent job and is performing it beautifully. He is back with his wife, and they are living happily together with the new Siamese cat they bought when they were reunited. For all practical purposes, the cat was the "enabler" in that family.

A pastor told me one time that he had become so concerned about a family which was going to pieces because of the husband's drinking, that when the husband was in his office on one occasion, he reached over the desk, grabbed him by the collar, picked him up, and said, "If you ever take another drink, I'm going to beat your head in!" That man never took another drink!

I certainly wouldn't advise that kind of intervention—that is unless you knew you could handle him if he did challenge you—but in that instance it worked. And in this business of working with alcoholics, we have a saying, "If it works, it's good!"

Every alcoholic will be reached and turned around in a different way, but I like to believe that however we do it, it is God working through us. Sometimes it may appear rather ruthless in order to strike deep and make a lasting impression. Then again, it may take only a word or two, carefully selected, to do the trick.

It has been said that life is a journey from God—to God. The alcoholic is on the same journey that every one of us is on, so when we work with him, try to call out that portion of his miraculous memory that will make his journey to God as pleasurable as possible.

Chapter VI

The Waiting Father

If there was ever a picture of bankruptcy—physical, mental, moral, social, spiritual, and any other—it was this picture of our young alcoholic friend getting up from the pig pen and starting for home.

Because he is bankrupt, we are only saying that he had lost something that he at one time had. Most alcoholics at one time were the picture of health, but the years of drinking and physical abuse leave the body flushed, trembling, broken, scarred, and prematurely aged.

The mental superiority that I suggested was a symbol of the alcoholic personality has been bankrupted through the drinking years until it is damaged in relationship to the years and amount of drinking.

Chronic alcoholism has taken a life that was upright and courageous and allowed it to drift into the sensual satisfactions of life.

Perhaps the social life of the alcoholic was never what it ought to have been in spite of the fact that he was the life of the party and a fellow who was jolly-well-met. Nonetheless, the years of this chemical abuse have driven him from the human race until he is lonesome in a crowd. Every alcoholic becomes a "lone drinker" sooner or later, if for no other reason than the charitable consideration that anyone who comes into contact with him is going to get hurt.

Every alcoholic, in like manner, becomes a spiritually bankrupt person. I have yet to meet a chronically alcoholic person who has kept a vital and committed relationship to God. In my experience, most of the alcoholics I have worked with had a better than average religious background. This means that they went to Sunday School as children and attended some church with their parents. They were, for all practical purposes, the children of God.

The vast majority of alcoholics whom I know are not ungodly people or unbelieving people. It's just that when you start to run, you run away from yourself, your loved ones, your society, and naturally you run away from God. This is the same unintentional disgust with God that the young man in our parable had for his Father and home.

This is the story of alcoholism: you fail to put first things first, and slowly but surely you lose what you have.

Alcoholics become spiritually bankrupt through carelessness and neglect, not through any positive unbelief. A vital relationship with

God can be lost just as easily through neglect as it can through outright rejection. Marriages are lost in the same way, through neglect and a failure to keep a relationship alive. In our relationship to God, as in marriage and other relationships, it isn't the great problems that tend to separate us but rather the little irritants, the sand-in-the-shoe kind of thing, coupled with the neglect that tends to widen the chasm they create.

All of this is involved in the life of this young man who trudges stoop-shouldered, dirty, and lonesome back toward his Father's house. I have yet to see any picture that could adequately portray this young man, nor words that could convey his despair. Yet down deep in that lonesome heart was a mustard seed of faith that believed going back would be better than continuing as he was.

What we witness here in our mind's eye is the surrender of a life. This young man believed that he could find the meaning of life by going out and WINNING his way. The rewards of life are only WON through SURRENDER! This is the only place where surrender means victory. When the old hymn says, "Make Me a Captive Lord, and Then I Shall Be Free," it is hitting the nail right on the head. Surrender means exchanging your own will and whims for that of another, hopefully a Power greater than your own. Instead of fighting to hold God off, it means letting go and letting Him in. Surrender means victory, because man's extremity brings God's opportunity.

Our young alcoholic friend is through calling the shots in our parable. It is here where I feel intervention and confrontation can stop the lunatics from running the asylum, or the sick from prescribing the healing. This manipulator must now let go and let God take over. The alcoholic must step down as the executive vice-president of the universe and turn the care and keeping of the universe back to God. This is no easy task for any man, much less for one who has become mentally preoccupied with a chemical that sends its victims out into the far reaches of grandiosity.

What better way can we explain the young man's dilemma in the parable than to say that he had lost his bargaining power. He was in no position to "wheel and deal" but now must await only the response of the Father.

There is no "dealing" with God! I wonder how often, because we know the end of this story, we come into the presence of God and deal with Him. Because we know that when we confess our sins, "He will forgive our sins and cleanse us from all unrighteousness" (I John 1: 9b), we tend to make our confessions and wait for Him to carry out His end of the bargain.

Whenever we come into the presence of God, we must do so in like manner with the young man in our text—as bankrupt people. Even when the hair is combed, and the clothes are neat, and no great social sin weighs heavy on our shoulders, we still must approach our Heavenly Father with the same attitude of heart and soul as the young man in our parable and be ready to confess, "Father, I am no longer worthy."

If I could have only one book for the rest of my life, it would be the Bible. If I could have only one portion of the Bible, it would be Jesus' parable of the Prodigal Son, because there is enough woven into this one simple story to enable anyone to live comfortably with God, himself, and his fellow man. If I could have only one portion of this parable, it would be the reunion of this wayward alcoholic son with his Father. Until any person hears this portion of the parable and lives this experience in his life, he will never begin to comprehend the incomprehensible Grace of God.

In our parable, Jesus tells us that while the young man was still a long way off the Father recognized him as his son, and what he saw filled him with compassion. This is the greatest moment of human history when the sinfulness of man is confronted by the holiness, the righteousness, the purity of God.

The Father had never stopped looking down the path and waiting—waiting—waiting. For sure, we have a waiting Father, one whose love goes with us over the years and the folly of our sin and rebellion.

When the Father recognizes the long lost

son, He runs to meet him and throws his arms around him and kisses him. We witness the loving of the unlovely. Think of how the son had embarrassed the "Stay-at-homes." Was there anything they hadn't suffered as the result of his behavior? Yet, see how he is accepted and loved. The love of the Father is greater than the sin of the son. So it is with each of us—the love God has for each of us is greater and stronger than any or all of the sin that so often holds us in its spell.

The Grace of God is unmerited love of God. This is the love God has for us in our bankrupt state of alcoholism or any other sick condition we may manifest.

I have often asked alcoholics, following an outpouring of their character defects, if God loves them. Many say they don't see how He can, or they only hope that He might.

Is there a greater privilege in the world than that which belongs to the person who, in this instant, is an ambassador for Christ, "God making his appeal through us" (II Corinthians 5:20b), and conveying the "Good News" that God loves us not because of what we are, but in spite of what we are?

For some this Gospel comes early and easy, and life is a joy. To others, like the alcoholic who must be battered from pillar to post, it comes later and hard. But come when it may, it is the greatest therapy in the world! When the Father reaches out and clutches his returning son, there is no thought that he had done anything wrong—only the assurance of the Father's forgiveness.

Guilt is a major factor in alcoholism like it is in any other life. What is the answer to guilt? Is it to live better today so you overcome the yesterday? Of course not. The answer to guilt has always been and will ever be, FORGIVENESS! Those who would apply the cosmetic salve to the guilt of the human soul only prolong the agony and drive it deeper into the inner recesses of the heart. The answer to guilt is forgiveness:

Listen to Isaiah:

> "Come now, let us reason together, says the lord:
> though your sins are like scarlet,
> they shall be as white as snow;
> though they are red like crimson,
> they shall become like wool." (Isaiah 1:18)

Listen to the Psalmist:

> "For as the heavens are high above the earth,
> so great is his steadfast love toward those who fear him;
> as far as the east is from the west,
> so far does he remove our transgressions from us.
> As a father pities his children,
> so the Lord pities those who fear him."
> (Psalm 103:11-13)

Listen to the author of Hebrews:

"For I will be merciful toward their
   iniquities,
and I will remember their sins no more."
(Hebrews 8:12)

To think that God can forget borders on blas-
phemy. Yet, we have just heard the author of
Hebrews reassure us that what we ask God to
forgive, He will forgive and then FORGET.

Christianity is not primarily goodness. It is
forgiveness! As Christians we are not getting
better and better. We, like the Prodigal, are the
objects of our Heavenly Father's love and acceptance to Himself. We are forgiven.

When we come into the presence of God
acknowledging our sin and unworthiness, we
have every right to expect Him to cast us out
and aside as the young fellow in our text undoubtedly expected to be when he arrived
home. When we hear Christ's ambassador say
that we are forgiven, it should come as a sur-
prise every time. Hunger is what makes something as commonplace as food look and taste
good. The reality of our phoniness is that which
makes the forgiveness of God such a wonderful
experience and in turn changes our lives.

God doesn't love us because we behave, or
because we are sober, or because we aren't in
trouble. God loves us—period!

The love of God is so great it is beyond man's
understanding. God loves us because He is
God, not because of what we are. You can't out-
hate, out-drink, out-hurt, out-raise hell, or out-

steal the love of God. The love of God is as constant as the sun. God loves you no matter what! It is precisely here where lives change. The young man didn't leave the pig pen because of the filth. He left because he was loved, and the miracle of memory reminded him of that.

What wonderful news for the alcoholic, in his pell-mell run from God, to hear that he is the object of God's love. There is no one in the world whom God loves any more than him. There is no quantity to the love of God. You can't have five gallons, or ten gallons, or fifteen gallons of God's love. If we are the objects of God's love, then it all belongs to each of us. What a relief to know that I don't have to impress Him or my fellow man with my imitated goodness, but now I can acknowledge my phoniness and let it be the very sign of God's love for my life.

The love of God for any man cannot change. The only thing that can change is our love for Him. I suppose there is no hurt in all the world that is worse than loving someone and not being loved in return. Sometimes we feel this with our children. We love them more than words can express, but there are times when it seems that our love is rejected. Oh, how nice it would be, if we could only stop loving our kids on some occasions when they are at their worst, but we can't. Even our human love will not let go.

Think how much greater the love is that God has for us and how less apt He is to let us go. One of the great frustrations of being a parent is not being able to stop loving, and this is what God must experience as we go our independent ways and proceed time and time again to fall on our faces.

The fact remains that nothing had changed regarding the love the Father had for his wayward son. His love was not greater or less; it was just there to meet him when he, and if he, returned.

We neither get what we expect or deserve when we return to our Heavenly Father. A little child said one time that he wanted someone to love him when he was naughty. This is exactly the kind of a God Jesus reveals to us in the parable. While we can anger God, embarrass Him, hurt Him like any child can do to his parents, we can never stop Him from loving us.

This is what St. Paul is saying to us when we read in his letter to the Christians in Rome: "For I am sure that neither death, nor life, nor angels, nor principalities, nor things present, nor things to come, nor powers, nor height, nor depth, nor anything else in all creation, will be able to separate us from the love of God in Christ Jesus our Lord." (Romans 8:38,39) As formidable a foe as alcoholism may be to the welfare of men's souls, the love of God is greater.

The Grace of God is the strongest, most

powerful force in the world and yet how often have we as the people of God talked and acted as though it were as fragile as crystal and as weak as tinsel. Christians drink ethyl alcohol like they participate in many other human activities, but when they start getting into trouble, there is a tendency to think that God is getting out of the picture. When the church talks of total abstinence as some kind of ideal, and raves about the scourge of "demon rum," you can rest assured that those who may get into trouble because of problem drinking or alcoholism will not seek out the church for help, because it has already in a very real sense prejudged them.

In this sense, I am led to believe that the various segments of the religious community that have attacked alcoholic beverage as something evil of and by itself, have really done more to create a millieu for alcoholism than they have done to prevent it.

Those segments of the Christian Church who have attempted to promote total abstinence from alcohol as the teaching of the Bible have created a spiritual and intellectual "credibility gap" in the church. While there are many excellent reasons for one being totally abstinent, misinterpretation of Scripture is not one of them. The Scriptures abhor drunkenness like any other irresponsible behavior, but nowhere do we see the Scriptures condemn drinking of and by itself.

We have been experts in establishing guilt, but have failed in applying the healing of the Gospel where it is needed most. If we aren't willing to reflect the healing love of God into the lives of men, then we have no right to point out the illness in the first place. Often we have talked about the Gospel and never really understood what it means.

When the waiting Father has kissed and embraced his son, put a cloak on his shoulders, the ring on his hand, shoes on his feet, and ordered the fatted calf to be killed and the feast prepared, he says something that proves in my mind that this son of his is alcoholic. He says, "For this my son was dead, and is alive again; he was lost, and is found." (Luke 15:24) If there is anyone who knows what it is to die and come alive again, it is the chronic alcoholic. Over the years I have heard many an alcoholic say they have prayed that God would let them die so they wouldn't have to awaken to see the people they have hurt, and acknowledge what they have done while intoxicated. To die and come alive is the story of the slide into alcoholism.

To say the alcoholic is lost is true! You are lost when you are out of control, when you are outside of the plan that God has for every life. It is beyond thinking to believe that something as valuable as a human life would be without a plan in God's sight. You are lost when you are lost to yourself and the plans you have for your own life. No alcoholic ever plans to get himself into the messes he does. The Father spoke well when he said his son who was dead and lost was now alive and found.

We must not lose sight of the fact that this entire parable does not primarily concern itself with this young man and his alcoholic behavior as much as it speaks of the Father and his faithfulness and love. All of us know only too well the kind of behavior we are capable of, if not in act then in meditation. Do we really know what our Heavenly Father is like? This is what Jesus wants us to know in this parable. What He is saying is that in spite of how terrible we have behaved, in spite of how far away from home we have gone, in spite of how long it has been since we left, the way back is open. When you question how God could love one like yourself, let Him be your judge for we are far more apt to be severe on ourselves than God is. His judgment is just, but it is also merciful.

This whole chapter under the title, "The Waiting Father," might be summed up in the words of a little boy who, when he had gotten disgusted with the way things were going for him around the house, informed his mother, "When I get old enough to find the way home, I'm going to run away."

How can we get to the countless lives who are running away from home through the various chemical mood modifiers and let them know that they don't have to run any more—that they are welcome home where they belong?

When the members of an Alcoholic Anonymous group welcome a person into their fellowship with only a desire to help that person stop drinking, they are opening their arms and welcoming a sick person into a healing environment. Haven't we too often within the religious community made health the standard by which we accept people into our midst? Isn't it time that we made it clear that Jesus came for the sick, the sinful, the outcast, the person who has all the feelings that I have and that you have?

When the flood of past wrongs crowd in upon us and the flashing sign of guilt keeps blinking in our minds, it is time to turn it off with the unmerited forgiveness of God and turn on the flashing sign that says, "Forgiven."

What is worse than going through life with a glance over your shoulder because of past wrongs? The healing, forgiving Grace of God awaits every one of us, just as it awaited the impetuous young man in our parable.

While alcoholism may be the worst illness in the world, it can be arrested and lives can be salvaged for God because all healing is of God. There is no illness so great that His power is not sufficient. To those who would suggest that God is dead, I would like to point to all arrested alcoholics, all are valid proof that God is very much alive in their lives, and they are alive and well as the result of God's healing in their lives.

Many an alcoholic has said to me, "Thank

God for my alcoholism because I had to learn how to live or I would have died."

If you are an alcoholic, or you know someone who is, never become so preoccupied with the manifestations of this illness that you fail to see or show that the Father is waiting to receive us back when we have become sick and tired of being sick and tired, as we all do when away from home.

Chapter VII

The Discipline of Home

Our young alcoholic friend of Jesus' parable made up his mind to live at home instead of away. He made up his mind to live instead of to die. He made up his mind to live a life of sobriety instead of the run-away life of chemical comforters. He made up his mind to accept the discipline of home instead of the unmanageable dictates of his passions and appetites.

When A.A. in the first of the twelve steps says, "We admitted we were powerless over alcohol—THAT OUR LIVES HAD BECOME UNMANAGEABLE," it is saying that this life had become undisciplined.

The alcoholic, in the vast majority of cases, is a rigid person. Right and wrong are just that! He is prompt for appointments and hates to arrive late for anything. He is a perfectionist in his work and is irritated by people who are careless and half-way in their work. He goes to work early and stays late, and tends to accept more than his share of the responsibility.

The alcoholic is rigid in discipline, but with

the advent of chronic alcohol dependency, this discipline is erroded until he arrives at a point when he doesn't care whether school keeps or not. More than one alcoholic has been so shocked upon looking at the lack of discipline that has taken place in his life that he sought help through treatment of A.A.

What A.A. is saying is that in a very carefully managed life, alcohol has created a very unmanageable situation that must be admitted, and some management and discipline restored. There must be discipline in every life if it is to function effectively at any level.

Now that the young man in our parable was back home, he would accept the discipline of his Father's household. Now, instead of seeing it as something that was confining and negative, he saw it as his real peace and liberty. He could see that out of this discipline would spring the many manifestations of his talents.

What a shame that we have so often given the idea that commitment to Christ is a confining and restrictive move in our lives instead of that which really frees us to live a Peace with God and enables us to do our "thing" in a place and way that only each individual can. I find that Jesus puts no restriction on our attempting great things even when we fail time and again. He was much more severe with the servant who did nothing with the talent that he was given than he was with those who risked their talents with the real possibility of failure.

Along these lines I have a philosophy that says I must do what I must do, and then ask God to forgive me. How often do we do what we must do, and we just aren't sure that we ought to have done it, and are not really sure whether it was right or wrong? I believe that when we attempt our best in this partnership with Christ, He is far more prone to be forgiving and understanding than we are with ourselves. How sad when through some warped theology we restrict the talent in anyone's life, and God is unable to reflect Himself through it as a result.

One of the MUST disciplines for the alcoholic who wishes to maintain sobriety, is attendance at a weekly A.A. meeting until he or she departs this life. As long as there is no cure for alcohol dependency, but only the possibility of arresting it, there must be a commitment to the fellowship of A.A. for as long as the alcoholic lives. Call A.A. what you will, it remains outpatient, peer-group therapy for a progressive illness even after years of sobriety.

The Christian who ignores or makes light of his continuing need for the Grace of God is one who is moving onto Spiritual thin ice. In like manner, the alcoholic who forgets the enormity of his mental and physical preoccupation with ethyl alcohol is going to make light of his need for the continuing, supportive help of A.A. Once again we see the danger of carelessness as the enabling factor in going back to drinking, as it may have been the enabling factor in the initial descent into alcoholism.

I believe that A.A. is as close to a guarantee of sobreity as anything can be a guarantee. There is nothing that has proven more effective in arresting this complex, multi-faceted illness in the past nor into the foreseeable future. Not only do we see its importance as a group or squad in the place where it meets during the week, but we also see it in those treatment facilities which are most effective, as it becomes the red thread that runs through the treatment philosophy.

In no way is that any kind of an attempt to belittle other treatment philosophies or professionals in this work, but the fact remains that no other effort has proven as successful as A.A.

When I say that A.A. is a guarantee to sobriety, it means, of course, when the Twelve Steps of A.A. are LIVED. Often you will hear a drinking alcoholic, or someone who is on a "dry drunk," say that A.A. isn't for him—he couldn't find sobriety in A.A. The reason for this, of course, is that he didn't live the program.

You don't have to like A.A., or even the people in it. You don't have to understand A.A. You don't have to agree with A.A. You don't have to exegete A.A. YOU HAVE TO LIVE IT! The closing words of the Twelve Steps of A.A. would point this out when they say, "and to *practice* these principles in all our affairs."

There isn't a person on earth who wouldn't be living an exemplary life, even if he had never had a drink, if he were LIVING the Twelve Steps of A.A.

When I run into someone who thinks that A.A. isn't for him, I either think of him as ignorant of the truth, one who wants to keep drinking, or as just plain phony. There are many who approve of the A.A. way of life, but do not themselves believe and live the program; therein lies the key to the success or failure of anyone in A.A.

This is precisely the place where there must be total commitment to the program of A.A. This is not some kind of Avon sample where you try it to see if you like it, but rather an all-out commitment. This is a parachute jumping experience where you place your life on the line with this program. Then you begin to live these Twelve Steps as simply and humbly as God gives the courage and strength. The alcoholic has no more right to say that any one of the Twelve Steps is less important than we have the right to suggest that any of the Ten Commandments is less important than another.

There are those who like to take A.A. cafeteria style, and "perform" those steps that seem easier and more applicable, and forget the others. A case in point is the Fifth Step of A.A. which says, "Admitted to God, to ourselves, and to another human being the exact nature of our wrongs." Naturally this is a difficult step because it must be preceded by a fear-less and searching moral inventory; and then, here in the Fifth Step, the alcoholic must ver-balize before another "human being" the exact nature of his wrongs.

I have no way of proving it, but as I put my ear to the ground in A.A. circles, I would guess that a considerable number of the members of A.A. have never taken what either they or I would consider a good Fifth Step. Certainly the quantity and quality of sobriety would improve if just such a step were more frequently lived.

I point out the Fifth Step as an example of one of the easy omissions in cafeteria style A.A. because this has been the chief area of my activ-ity with the alcoholic. It is important, too, be-cause we find it in the midst of the Twelve Steps and a step that gives great strength to that which goes before and comes after. There is tremendous therapy in the Fifth Step of A.A., and I have seen many alcoholics turn A.A. from something that helps them quit drinking into a meaningful way of life because of a good Fifth Step.

There is a statement I have remembered over the years that says, "Impression Without Ex-pression Leaves Depression," which I find most helpful in understanding of the Fifth Step in A.A., and of equal importance to the Chris-tian's need for Confession. What you verbalize to another human being, preferably a clergy-man in most instances, will tend never to plague you again. It's those things that we dam up inside ourselves to ferment and poison that do the greatest damage and tend to manifest themselves in hurtful ways elsewhere. I have a feeling, too, that you can take the first Five Steps of A.A. sitting in a chair, but when the Fifth Step has been lived, you have to get out of that chair to live and practice the rest.

I believe that these steps are the Voice of God as He spoke through those who laid them down for victims of this peculiar illness. I cannot emphasize enough how deeply I believe these steps are to be lived, as over against being agreed to or approved. That A.A. group will be serving the group best that makes one of the Twelve Steps the center of its conversation and concern in each squad or group meeting.

Attendance at the A.A. meeting is perhaps the discipline that must supersede all the rest—if there is such a thing. To *GO* to the meeting—to make that little "pilgrimage" each week—has a therapeutic effect on the life of the alcoholic. It provides a goal to look forward to in the intervening days and a sense of satisfaction when it has been attended.

Sometimes it is hard to attend because the weather is bad, the distance is long, there are those who may dominate the meeting, there are those who drink after the meeting is over, and all the other reasons why it would be convenient, if not easier, to stay home. The greater the desire to stay away, the greater is the need to attend! I think we often discover that is perhaps the one we gain the most from. When that little voice says, "Stay Home!" *GO!!*

I will sit still for only two reasons for the alcoholic missing A.A.—one is that he is so genuinely ill that he is unable to attend. The other is that he died during the week! No alcoholic will ever drink because he missed a meeting that he could not make, but there is real danger in missing a meeting that he could have made. Until alcoholism can be cured, I feel I must hold fast to this rather rigid position on A.A.

Another of the great disciplines that I believe essential for every alcoholic who returns "home" to sobriety, is getting back to a worship experience and into the religious community of believing people.

First, of course, is the basic need within each of us to worship God. We need this pause to recognize, adore, and magnify our Creator, our Redeemer, our Sustainer. It says of Jesus in Luke 4:16: "and he went to the synagogue, AS HIS CUSTOM WAS, on the sabbath day." What was such an important discipline for our Lord certainly cannot be of lesser importance to any one of us. The alcoholic needs what the worship experience has to offer as badly as any others who attend, and certainly there is no one who should be any more welcome than the alcoholic who is attempting to establish a new way of life to overcome his chemical dependency.

When I was a parish pastor at Redeemer Lutheran Church in White Bear Lake, Minnesota, one of my parishioners commented that a friend of hers referred to Redeemer as that church where all the "drunks" go. In our desires for respectability and acceptance, that statement kind of hurt, but then after a second thought, I told my wife, Shirley, that it was perhaps the finest compliment we had ever been paid. After all, they said of Jesus that he was "a friend of tax collectors and sinners!" (Luke 7:34b) And that was, in essence, what the lady was saying of this parish which had opened its doors and welcomed alcoholics to worship and membership in the Congregation.

The alcoholic on the way to total rehabilitation needs to know the joy that was the Psalmist's when he said, "I was glad when they said to me, 'Let us go to the house of the Lord!' " (Psalm 122:1) The alcoholic needs to feel a part of the corporate household of God's people and to participate in the ministry of Word and Sacrament. I believe that if there is a thirst that exceeds the thirst for alcohol in the alcoholic, it is the thirst for God.

The need to return to the religious persuasion of his choice is to keep clear the fact that neither A.A. nor the church is a substitute for the other. A.A., from its beginning to this day, has never attempted to be a substitute for the church. Nor, on the other hand, does the church believe that it can substitute itself for A.A. For the alcoholic to choose one over the other is like choosing between exhaling and inhaling. Both have distinct purposes, and they should ever be so. There is no question but what both A.A. and the church have looked upon each other with suspicion, but never has there been greater respect for each other than exists today. This relationship is improving all the time.

Perhaps the finest comment I have ever heard about A.A. in this respect is that slogan which says: "A.A. didn't open the gate of Hell and let me out, nor did it open the gate of Heaven and let me in; but it did keep me sober long enough to decide which way I wanted to go." The church of any creed is never better than when it opens its facilities to be used by A.A., and then opens its arms to the alcoholic who chooses to identify with God's children in that particular congregation.

What goes on in a church is as important to the satisfaction of the worshipper's needs as what goes on in A.A. is to the alcoholic. But, like A.A., the need to make the pilgrimage to that particular place of worship is the first and most important discipline. The liturgy may not always be understandable, the hymns may be a bit of a drag, the sermon may not have hit the mark, but the fact remains that you have gathered in that place where our Lord has promised, "Where two or three are gathered in My name, there am I in the midst of them." (Matthew 18:20) If there is any effort whatsoever

105

made to worship, whether it be in a small frame church in a coulee on the plains, or in the impressive cathedral on the avenue of a great city, there will be a sense of satisfaction and self-respect as one leaves that experience.

Remember, you don't go to church to get God's love or approval. You go because of a prior love and redemptive act on His part. To go to church "in-order-to get God to love you" is an imperative ethic or behavior, and nothing could be more wrongly inspired and unnecessary. On the other hand, when you enter the church on the sabbath "because God loves you," you are demonstrating an indicative ethic or behavior which is really the only motive for being there at all. When you begin to evaluate the love that God has for us, it takes times like sabbath worship to reflect anew on the height and breadth and depth of this fantastic love of God.

Another discipline is that of "prayer and meditation" as suggested in Step Eleven of A.A. This is the time of day when we stop to remember to put first things first. To read something, to pray, or just meditate to improve the conscious contact with God is a healing and growth situation. How simple a discipline it is to set a few moments aside every day for that "quiet hour" when we reflect on what life is really all about.

We need to get away, not geographically, but mentally, and take a look at ourselves. We need to step back in order that we might be our own clergyman, our own doctor, our own psychologist, our own A.A. counselor, our own friend who sets us right when we are wrong, and gives glory to God at seeing so much that is right.

For over a decade I have intensively watched alcoholics from the vantage point of treatment, A.A. and the church, get well, stop drinking, and achieve sobriety. In those same years I have watched from the vantage point as others kept drinking, died, or remained in the morass of the most terrible disease known to mankind.

"Who makes it?" we ought to ask. The people who make it are those who want sobriety more than life, more than God, more than family, or more than anything else. When they want it that badly, they find in A.A. that peer-group fellowship that speaks like no other. They find in the church that open door to the fellowship of Word and Sacrament, and then prayer and meditation become a natural response to the mysteries of God's Grace.

When Jesus' disciples became concerned about who was to be the greatest in the Kingdom of Heaven, Jesus took a little child, put him in their midst, and said, "Unless you turn and become like children, you will never enter the kingdom of heaven." (Matthew 18:3)

So often we are childish, but so seldom childlike. Yet childlikeness is what our Lord desires to find in each of us. Jesus said that if any of us, whoever we might be, wishes to see the kingdom of heaven, we must become like a little child.

It is difficult, if not impossible, to say what it is that brings the miracle of sobriety to the chronic alcoholic, but a least one of the elements present is a childlikeness as he confronts the enormity of the illness, the simplicity of the A.A. way of life, and the abundant mercy that God holds out to him in the person of Jesus Christ.

If we could speak to the alcoholic Prodigal whom we have followed in the parable, or to any arrested alcoholic, who in childlike simplicity has accepted this illness and healing, he would say in some different but identical way what another said when he was healed by the Mender of broken men, "One thing I know, that though I was blind, now I see." (John 9:25b)